MY RAMADAN FUN BOOK

**PUZZLES
CROSSWORDS
WORDSEARCHES
COLOURING
AND MANY OTHER ACTIVITIES**

by
TAHERA KASSAMALI

Goodword**kidz**

Helping you build a family of faith

Islamic Funbooks

RAMADHAN

Children need to be taught Islam in a way which takes into consideration the mind of a child. Learning about religion is sometimes taken as serious and even boring. In order to change that negative conception, educators and parents need to use more appealing methods to put the message of Islam across to the younger generation. This book has been designed with that purpose in mind, and we hope that both parents and children will enjoy going through it.

For the parent

Our experience show that no book or teacher can take the place of a parent when it comes to teaching children religious beliefs and practices. We urge that parents use this book as a tool in their efforts to help their children understand and appreciate Islam. The following points are suggested:

1 The activities in this book cater for various levels. Some children may be able to do them easily, while some may require help with a few pages. Work together with your child through these pages to encourage an enthusiasm for learning and thinking about Islamic teachings. Rather than providing all the answers, help him/her to think, and perhaps refer to a book where the answers to a particular exercise may be available.

2. Reinforce the concepts taught in this book during the holy month of Ramadhan. The Du'a for Iftar, for example, could be recited aloud by a family member each night in Ramadhan. Such practical implementation of the lessons in this book will ensure the child's understanding of its contents.

3. Some of the exercises require a reference to the Qur'an. Obtain a Qur'an with a simple translation for your child. Referring to the Qur'an will, Inshallah, encourage an interest in its contents, and an appreciation for the holy Book.

Please continue to encourage your child to learn more about Islam. To instil an appreciation for religious beliefs and practices in a young mind is the most rewarding thing you can do for your child. The effects could last a lifetime.

Rajab 1416/ December 1995.

Tayyiba Publishers
P.O.Box 88003, Lansdowne Mall
Richmond, B.C. Canada V6X 3T6

First published by Goodword Books 2003
in arrangment with Tayyiba Publishers and Distributors
Reprinted 2022
© Goodword Books 2022

Goodword Books
A-21, Sector 4, NOIDA-201301, Delhi NCR, India
Tel. +91 120 4131448, Mob. +91-8588822672
email: info@goodwordbooks.com
www.goodwordbooks.com

Altaf climbs the wall

1. Muslims recite a lot of the _____ during the month of Ramadhan.

2. The holiest night of the month of Ramadhan is _____.

3. Sura al-_____ says that this holy night is better than a thousand months.

4. _____ is the meal at the end of the fast.

5. Most Muslims break their fast with _____.

6. Battle of Badr was fought by the Muslims against the _____ of Mecca.

7. Many Muslims go to the _____ at night during Ramadhan.

8. The Prophet (s) has said that Ramadhan comes with _____ and _____ from Allah.

9. _____ is the migration of the Prophet (s) from Mecca to Medina.

10. _____ul_____ is celebrated after Ramadhan.

Altaf is playing with his friends. They want to see who can climb up the wall the fastest. The rule of the game is to answer the questions on the wall as they climb.

Altaf really wants to win. Help him climb quickly by filling in the blanks.

THE NEW MOON

Muslims follow the LUNAR CALENDAR.
This means the calendar is based
on the movement of the moon.
Allah says in the Holy Qur'an:
And they ask you about the new moon;
say they are indications of signs fixed for
mankind, and for the pilgrimage. (2:189)
Before the order to follow the moon was
given, Muslims followed the SOLAR
CALENDAR, just like other people. This
means they did not depend on the moon
for the beginning of the new month. The
SOLAR CALENDAR follows the sun, and
the numbers of days in the month are fixed.

Answer the following questions about the
LUNAR CALENDAR of the Muslims.

1. __Lunar__ is the first month of the Islamic calendar.

2. A Lunar month has either __20?__ or __31?__ number of days.

3. The full moon is usually around the __Subeath__ of the lunar month.

4. The Lunar year is shorter than the Solar year by __20?__ days.

5. The Islamic Lunar Calendar is dated from the time of the _____
   of the Holy Prophet (s).

Time
To
Think!!

What would happen if Muslims
followed the Solar calendar instead
of the Lunar? How would it affect
their fasting in Ramadhan?

Welcoming the Month of Allah

Muslims all over the world welcome Ramadhan.
It brings us blessings and happiness.

Color the sign below and then complete the letter.

Dear Ramadhan,
I am very happy to see you.
I like you because I hav yummy food!!!! food!!!! I have Yummy

From,
_____

Du'a for Iftaar

Say the following Du'a before you break your fast. Iftaar time is also a special time for seeking forgiveness of sins, and for asking for one's needs from Allah.

بِسْمِ اللّٰهِ الرَّحْمٰنِ الرَّحِيْمِ

In the name of Allah, the Beneficent, the Merciful.

اَللّٰهُمَّ لَكَ صُمْتُ

O Allah, I have fasted for You

وَ عَلٰى رِزْقِكَ اَفْطَرْتُ

And I break my fast on food provided by You

وَ عَلَيْكَ تَوَكَّلْتُ

And on You I rely.

Catch a Fish

Draw a line from the question to the correct answer.

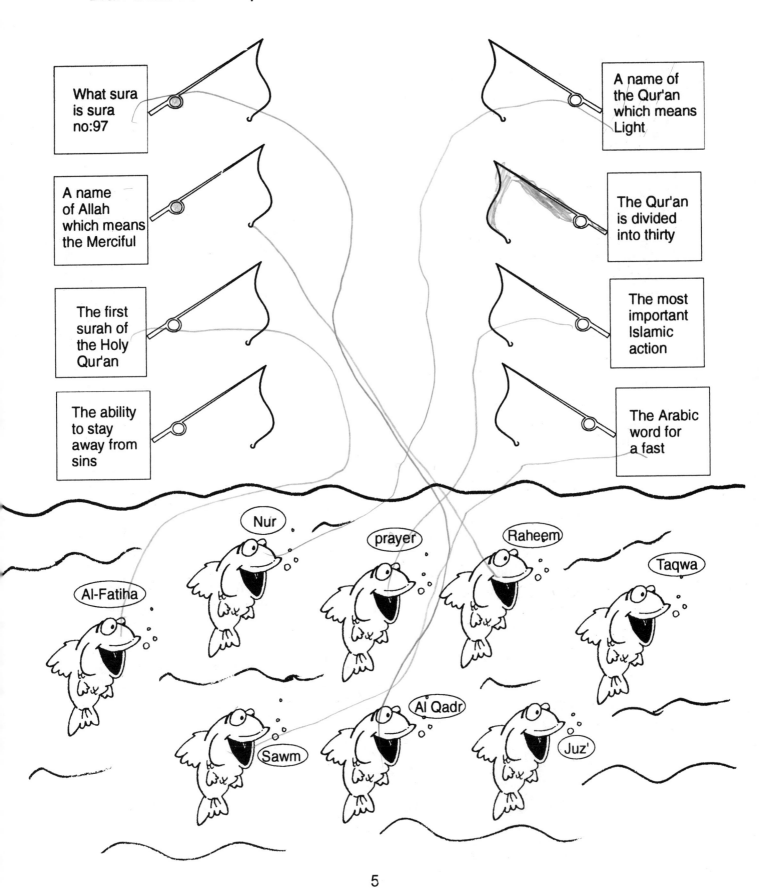

What sura is sura no:97

A name of Allah which means the Merciful

The first surah of the Holy Qur'an

The ability to stay away from sins

A name of the Qur'an which means Light

The Qur'an is divided into thirty

The most important Islamic action

The Arabic word for a fast

Nur

prayer

Raheem

Taqwa

Al-Fatiha

Al Qadr

Sawm

Juz'

A Word Puzzle

In the following puzzle a new word is got at every step by changing one letter only. To help you know which letter to change a clue is given for each step. The final two words will complete the sentence below.

L	O	S	T		P	L	A	N
1.					1.			
2.					2.			
3.					3.			
4.					4.			

Clues

1. Sura an-Nas is the _____ sura of the Holy Qur'an.

2. To be truly grateful to Allah, make a _____ of all the blessings He has given you.

3. Your body has been created in a wonderful way. The hand can be turned into many positions. When people are angry or tense they clench their hands into a _____.

4. A _____ is a form of worship of Allah which teaches us to control ourselves, and to think of the poor.

1. The Holy Prophet (s) came from the _____ of Banu Hashim.

2. Shaytan thought he was better than the human being because the human being has been created from _____ while he is created from fire.

3. Allah says in the Holy Qur'an that the life of this world is nothing but a sport and _____.

4. Allah promises us in the Qur'an that if we _____ to Him, He will answer us.

In Ramadhan, we _____ during the day and _____ during the night.

Zahid's Billboard

Zahid is a government worker in an Islamic country. He has been told to put a huge billboard in his area to announce details about Ramadhan. It seems, however, that he has missed some words. Choose from the following words to fill in the blank spaces on Zahid's Billboard.

Dates   Day   Laylatul Qadr   Moon   Juz'   Eid   Mosques.

The Holy month of Ramadhan is coming. If the _____ is seen on Tuesday night, Wednesday will be the first of Ramadhan. All hotels will be closed during the _____ will be open all night so that people can worship throughout the special nights of Ramadhan. At sunset there will be prayers at all the Mosques. _____ will be given for those who wish to break their fast before they reach home. One _____ of Qur'an will be recited every night at the Mosques. Schools and offices will be closed after _____ so that people can stay awake during that entire holy night. Details of celebrations will be announced later. WISHING YOU ALL A HAPPY AND BLESSED RAMADHAN

The Masjid

The Masjid is a very holy place. It is a place where people remember and worship Allah. The word Masjid means a place for prostration, or Sajdah.

During Ramadhan many Muslims go to the Masjid every night. They pray there and seek blessings and forgiveness from Allah during these special times. Because Allah has promised a great reward for Ibadah (worship) during Ramadhan, Muslims try to worship Allah more during the nights of Ramadhan. They know that it is a special chance to earn the pleasure of Allah.

Do you know what Allah says about a Masjid in the Qur'an?
Below are two ayats about the Masjid. Check them in your own Qur'an.

And the Mosques belong to Allah; so do not call upon anyone with Allah. (72:18)

Only he shall stay in the Masjid who believes in Allah and the last Day, and keeps up prayer and pays the Zakat, and fears none but Allah; perhaps these may be of the guided ones. (9:18)

Do you know these special Masjids? Write the name of each Masjid under the picture.

Masjid Manners

Sometimes children forget that while in the Masjid they need to respect the place. They don't remember their Masjid Manners. Fill in the blanks below to make sure you know your Masjid Manners. Choose your answers from the table below.

Don't be a Little Monkey ..

Please don't be a little monkey
when you are at the Masjid,
don't _____ or _____
and please don't ever _____ about.

If you see some _____ in the Masjid
please throw it in the bin.
Don't make the holy place a _____
please help to keep it _____.

Do keep _____ at prayer times,
and _____ when it's sermon time.
Greet all the Muslims at the Masjid
and say _____ with a _____.

Remember that the Masjid is
a place to _____ and _____.
And most of all, please don't forget,
the place belongs to _____.

Garbage, pray, run, clean, quiet, smile,
jump, salaam alaykum, mess, listen,
learn, God, shout.

9

Manners of reciting Qur'an

There are Manners for everything.
 MANNERS for eating.
 MANNERS for drinking.
 MANNERS for talking.

To be able to do things correctly, we need to know HOW to do it. This is what is known as MANNERS.

Reciting Qur'an also has its MANNERS. Because the Qur'an is a holy Book from Allah, we have to be very careful of HOW we recite it. Do you know some of the MANNERS of Qur'an recitation? The Qur'an itself tells us some of them. Look up the following ayats and then fill in the chart below.

Ayats

56:79

16:98

73:4

75:16

Manners of Qur'an Recitation

1.

2.

3.

4.

Learning Surah Numbers

Test your knowledge of the names and numbers of the surahs of the Holy Qur'an by filling in the following crossword.

Clues.

Across.

1. Sura Yasin is sura no: _____. of the Holy Qur'an.
3. Sura no. _____ is named after the Prophet who was swallowed by a whale.
4. Sura al-Ikhlas is sura no._____.
5. The moon is known as Qamar in Arabic. It is the name of sura no. _____.
8. Ramadhan is the ___th month of the Islamic calendar.
9. There are more than _____ verses in the Holy Qur'an (to the nearest thousand).

Down.

1. Sura no. _____ is named *The Romans*.
2. The Islamic Calendar has _____ months.
3. The Prophet who built the Ka'aba with his son has a sura named after him. It is sura no._____.
4. There are _____ surahs in the Qur'an.
5. The letter ق is the first letter in a sura named after that letter. It is sura no. ____
6. Sura no._____ is named *The Disbelievers* and discusses how the believers cannot worship the gods of the disbelievers.
7. The event of the elephants attacking the Ka'aba is discussed in sura no. ____.

11

A Train to fill . . .

Fill in the blanks on the train carriages by choosing the answers from the box below.

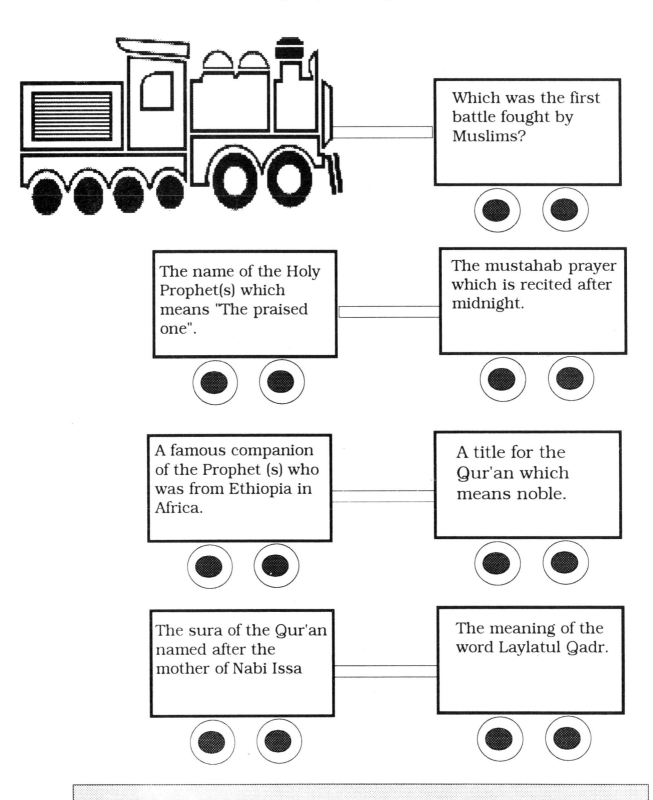

Which was the first battle fought by Muslims?

The name of the Holy Prophet(s) which means "The praised one".

The mustahab prayer which is recited after midnight.

A famous companion of the Prophet (s) who was from Ethiopia in Africa.

A title for the Qur'an which means noble.

The sura of the Qur'an named after the mother of Nabi Issa

The meaning of the word Laylatul Qadr.

Night of Power, Maryam, Al-Kareem, Bilal
Muhammad, Tahajjud, Badr

 # Fruits of Fasting

Fasting is not always easy.
Sometimes we get hungry and thirsty.
We get tired and sleepy.
These are the efforts that we put in Ramadhan to get the benefits.

Ramadhan is like a garden. When a gardener puts in efforts to look after his garden, he gets beautiful flowers, or fruits.
Our efforts in Ramadhan will also bear us some beautiful fruits.

Under each of the fruits below, write one benefit we get from fasting. You may choose some from the list at the bottom.

Taqwa, self-control, kindness, sympathy, charity, goodness
nearness to Allah, strength, sincerity, forgiveness, blessings.

13

Two Different families . . .

This family seems very happy. They have plenty to eat and their joy can be seen in their faces.

This family may not be so happy. They have very little to eat. How do you think their faces might look? Draw their eyes and mouths to show how you think their expressions might be.

Hunger around the World

It is a terrible thing to be hungry and have no food. When you get hungry while fasting, you know there is delicious food waiting for you at Iftaar time. Think of all the hungry children around the world who have nothing, or very little, to eat. Life must be very difficult for them.

The maps below have some countries in which there are many suffering children.

These children suffer from hunger and thirst. Some of them have seen a lot of misery and death, and some have lost their homes. Please remember them in your prayers.

To find out the names of some of these countries, unscramble the names beside each map. Write the correct name, and then try to find the country in the map.

AFRICA

IOHPAIET _____

DSANU _____

QMBAZUOIEM _____

EUROPE

NISOBA _____

INOMAAR _____

ASIA

RIAQ _____

GDENBHLAAS _____

What can we do ?

Many people wonder what they can do for the hungry children around the world. The Holy Qur'an tells us many things that we can do. There are some things we can do for them, and some we can do for ourselves so that we are not guilty of ignoring the hunger in the world.

Below are the number of four ayats of the Holy Qur'an. Each ayat will give you a suggestion of what you could do. Read the ayat, look at the clues in the circles, and then write what <u>you</u> can do in the fight against hunger.

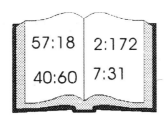

57:18	2:172
40:60	7:31

Charity

Du'a

Waste

Thanks

Four Suggestions

1.

2.

3.

4.

A Table full of Food

Ahmad was reading in his room when he _____ the Adhan

of Maghrib from the nearby _____. It was time to pray

and then break his fast. Ahmad went to the bathroom to do

_____. He said his prayers and then went down for Iftaar. The

_____ was full of food. His mother had made _____

and _____. There was _____ and

many different _____. Ahmad's favourite was the

_____. Ahmad sat down in his _____ and said

the _____ for Iftaar. He thought of all the hungry

_____ in the _____. *Thank you,*

_____, he said. *Thank you for all the* _____

You have given us. Please help those who are hungry and have no

food. And Guide us to help them in whatever way we can.

17

A Special Month

Write the words that match the clues. The letters in the boxes will tell you the name of a special Islamic month.

1. Five of these everyday will keep you connected with Allah and help you stay away from bad deeds.

2. The name of Allah which means He is forgiving and will forgive us our sins if we truly repent.

3. The Muslim way of greeting other Muslims which is also a du'a for them.

4. The first battle fought by Muslims against the Quraysh of Mecca. The Muslims won even though the enemies were stronger.

5. The fast for Muslims begins from this time

6. The early morning meal which is taken by those who wish to fast.

7. It is the sunnah of the Prophet (s) to break the fast with this.

8. The Muslim call for prayers, which invites people to come to pray.

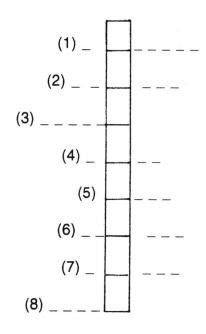

(1) _ □ _ _ _ _ _

(2) _ _ □ _ _ _

(3) _ _ _ _ □

(4) _ □ _ _

(5) □ _ _ _

(6) _ _ □ _ _ _

(7) _ □ _ _ _

(8) _ _ _ _ □

18

HOLY RAMADHAN

Ramadhan
Timings

Timings are very important for a person who wishes to fast.
We need to know the time when the fast begins and the time when it ends.
We also need to know the time for Salat so that we can say our prayers on time.
For each of the clocks below, draw the hands to show the correct time.
Use the timings of tomorrow's fast.

Suhoor

Subh prayer

Iftaar

Maghrib prayer

Holy Qur'an on Ramadhan

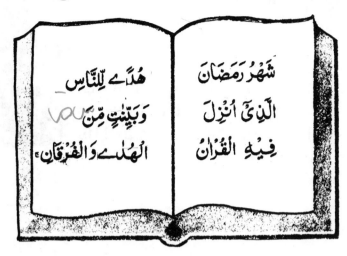

The Holy Qur'an talks about fasting and the month of Ramadhan in Sura al-Baqarah. Read the translation of ayats 183-185 of Al-Baqarah in your Qur'an and then answer the following questions.

1. According to these ayats, what is the most important result of fasting?

_____

2. Give an example of someone who is allowed not to fast in Ramadhan.

_____

3. What happened in the month of Ramadhan to make it very special?

_____

4. Give two titles of the Holy Qur'an given in these verses.

_____

5. What two things should you do at the end of Ramadhan?

_____

DU'A

Du'a is a communication with Allah. By allowing us to pray to Him, Allah has given us the keys to His treasures. He has allowed us to knock at His door and ask Him for our needs.

Through Du'a we:
1. Praise and thank Allah for His blessings.
2. Ask for our needs.
3. Complain of our troubles.
4. Seek forgiveness for our sins.
Best of all, through Du'a we establish a very close relationship with our Creator.

Du'a is a source of strength and power for the believer.
Believers know that by praying to Allah they can have success in the world and the hereafter.

In the Qur'an there are many beautiful verses in which Allah invites us to pray to Him. Read the following verses and think :

Who is it who answers the distressed when he calls unto Him, and removes the distress, and makes you the successors on the earth? Is there any god other than Allah? How little you reflect.

27:62

Your Lord says: Call to me, I will answer you. Surely those who are too proud to worship me shall enter Hell, disgraced.

40:60

And when My servants ask you about Me, then (say) Surely, I am near. I answer the prayer of the supplicant when he prays to me. So they should hear my Call, and believe in me, so that they may be led aright.

2:186

WHY DO WE DO DU'A?

Each of the following ships has one reason why we do Du'a. The letters however, are scrambled. Unscramble the word and fill in the blank under it.

To _____ Allah

To seek _____

To ask for our _____

To be _____ to Allah

To _____ Allah

To get _____ in both the worlds

Ramadhan Wordsearch

Can you find the following words:
Qur'an, Du'a, Tasbih, Fast, Qadr, Subh, Maghrib, Iftar, Food, Blessings, Mercy, Forgive, Kind, Help, Mosque.

P	F	O	S	Q	E	E	K	I	N	D	T
S	F	P	M	A	G	H	R	I	B	E	A
U	O	M	O	S	Q	U	E	P	T	E	S
B	R	B	L	E	S	S	I	N	G	S	B
O	G	M	O	N	P	S	H	E	L	T	I
R	I	E	M	Q	U	R	A	N	L	T	H
O	V	R	O	B	E	I	L	F	A	S	T
O	E	C	H	T	R	Q	S	O	H	E	L
D	N	Y	B	T	E	A	D	O	I	S	P
I	M	L	A	A	U	D	I	D	U	Q	S
E	H	E	L	P	V	R	I	F	T	A	R
L	Q	U	T	I	F	R	B	E	O	L	P

24

The Gifts of Ramadhan

Ramadhan is a very special GUEST,
A friend who brings comfort and joy into our homes,
A welcome guest who is awaited eagerly,
and missed when it leaves.

A guest often brings gifts for us. Ramadhan also comes with many gifts from Allah. Can you think of some?

If the gifts below are what Ramadhan would bring to your home, what would they contain? Make a label for each of them. You may choose from the ones in the box.

Mercy, Blessings, Thawab, Hope
Forgiveness, Love, Peace
Happiness, Kindness.

 # Wise Words of the Holy Prophet (s)

It is narrated that once, when Ramadhan was approaching, the Holy Prophet Muhammad (s) gave a sermon in which he explained to Muslims about the importance of Ramadhan. He advised Muslims how to behave while fasting so that their fast would be accepted and they would receive the Mercy of Allah. Read and think about some of the things he said:

O people! The month of Allah has come with His mercies and blessings. This is the month that is the best of months according to Allah. Its days are among the best of days. Its nights are among the best of nights.

While fasting, remember the hunger and thirst on the Day of Judgement.

Guard your tongues against unworthy words, and your eyes from unworthy scenes, and your ears from sounds that should not be heard.

Do raise your hands at the time of prayer, as it is the best time for asking for His mercy.

O People! . . . your back is breaking under the heavy load of your sins, so prostrate yourself before Him for long intervals and make it lighter.

Anyone who treats others well during this month, Allah will send His mercy on him in Quiyamat, and anyone who mistreats others in this month, Allah will keep him away from His mercy.

O People! The gates of Paradise remain open in this month. Do pray that the gates may not be closed on you. While the gates of Hell are closed, do pray to Allah that these gates may never be opened.

Questions

1. What does the Prophet (s) say about the Day of Judgement?

_____

_____

2. Give two types of unworthy speech you should stop your tongue from:

X —————————————————————

X —————————————————————

3. What type of unworthy sound should you stop your ear from hearing?

X —————————————————————

4. How can you make the burden of your sins less?

_____

5. What should you pray for during this month?

_____

_____

Joining Sentences

Join each part of column A to a part in column B to make a complete sentence.

A	**B**
1. Ramadhan is the ninth month	to thank Allah for His Guidance during Ramadhan.
2. Zakatul Fitr	is not obligatory on a traveller.
3. A sick person	lying, backbiting etc.
4. Fasting in Ramadhan	Forgiveness and Mercy.
5. Fasting helps us to	does not fast in Ramadhan but gives Qadha during the year.
6. While fasting we should stay away from	of the Islamic Calendar.
7. Ramadhan is a month of	control ourselves.
8. We celebrate Eid	is taken out for the poor before the Eid prayer.

Put the Sheep in their Barns

Help Farmer Abdul put his sheep in their barns. The sentences on the sheep will tell you where they go. The ones with a True sentence will go in the barn with the doors marked ✔. The ones with a False sentence will go in the barn with the doors marked ☒. Draw a line from each sheep to its barn.

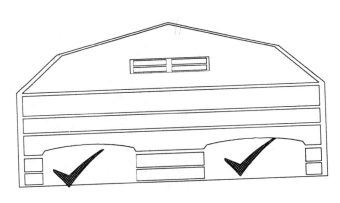

The Qur'an has 166 Surahs

Zakat means to give charity

We fast in Ramadhan so we can lose weight

Taqwa is the ability to stay away from sins

The 99 names of Allah are called Asma-ul-Husna

The Prophet (s) received his first revelation in Medina

Eid-ul-Adha is celebrated after Ramadhan

A Writing Exercise

Look at the pictures below. Beside each picture there are words which you may think of when looking at that picture. Using some of those words, write a few sentences about each picture.

Allah,
worship
pray
quiet
respect
meet
learn

_____
_____
_____
_____
_____
_____

_____
_____
_____
_____
_____

Holy
revealed
guidance
laws
recite
arabic
wisdom.

Prayer,
five
wudhu,
qibla,
time,
slowly,
important,

_____
_____
_____
_____
_____
_____

Allah is worshipped in many different ways. The acts of worship are called Ibadah. Ibadah is a very important part of a Muslim's life, because it is through Ibadah that we communicate with Allah, praise Him and thank Him for all he has blessed us with. Have you heard of the follwing Ibadah? Describe them briefly in the space provided and then find them in the wordsearch below.

Salat _____

Tilawatul Qur'an _____

Du'a _____

Zikr _____

Tasbih _____

B	S	H	I	R	S	U	T
S	T	A	S	B	I	H	P
A	W	D	E	Q	L	U	A
L	U	M	O	U	D	S	H
A	Z	I	K	R	V	E	T
T	H	I	D	A	P	L	E
M	O	F	E	N	W	E	A

A Very Special Night

In Ramadhan there is a very special night.
Write the first letter for each of the following pictures to get the name of that night. Then answer the questions below.

_____ _____ _____ _____ _____ _____ _____ _____

_____ _____ _____ _____

1. What does the name mean?

2. When is this night?

3. What happened on this night?

An Acrostic Poem

Do you know what an Acrostic poem is? It is a poem made from the letters of a word. Each letter of the word begins a line in the poem.

Haleema made the following Acrostic poem from the word MUSLIM.

Making others happy,
Understanding our faith,
Speaking only the truth,
Learning all that is good,
Increasing our knowledge,
Makes Allah pleased.

Try to make an Acrostic poem on the word RAMADHAN.

R _____

A _____

M _____

A _____

D _____

H _____

A _____

N _____

Which Way will you go ???

You can choose to go on different paths during your life.
You can choose to go on a path TOWARDS Allah.
You can choose to go on a path AWAY from Allah.
The path TOWARDS Allah is known as the Sirat al-Mustaqim
or the straight path.
Each path has certain actions which lead to it.

The box below shows certain actions, some of which lead to the
Sirat al-Mustaqim, while others lead to the path away from Allah.
Join each action to its path.

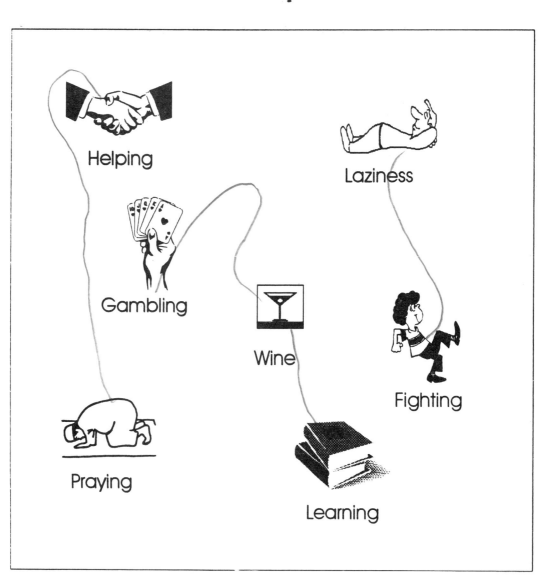

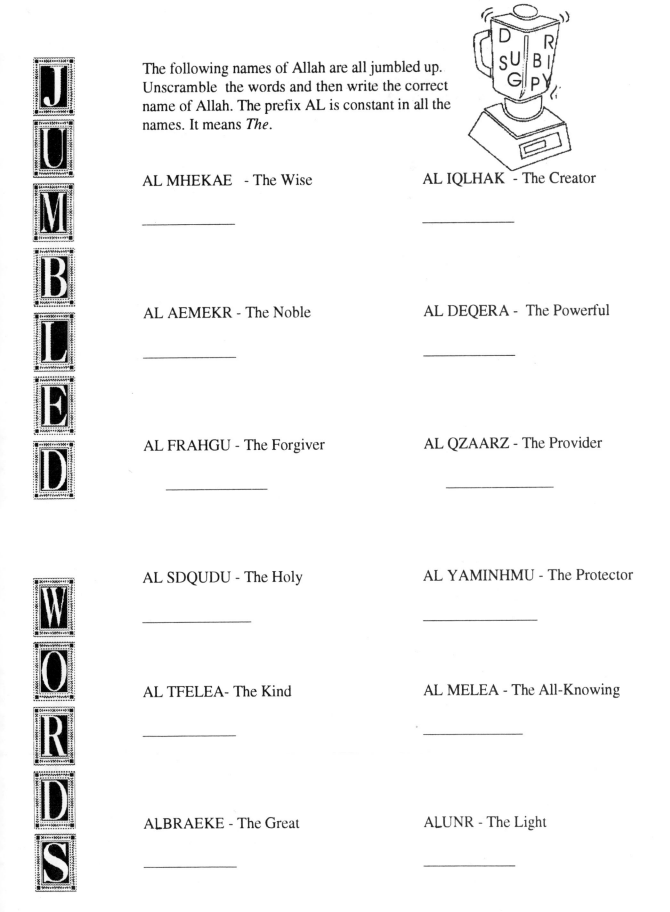

The following names of Allah are all jumbled up. Unscramble the words and then write the correct name of Allah. The prefix AL is constant in all the names. It means *The*.

AL MHEKAE   - The Wise

_____

AL IQLHAK - The Creator

_____

AL AEMEKR - The Noble

_____

AL DEQERA - The Powerful

_____

AL FRAHGU - The Forgiver

_____

AL QZAARZ - The Provider

_____

AL SDQUDU - The Holy

_____

AL YAMINHMU - The Protector

_____

AL TFELEA- The Kind

_____

AL MELEA - The All-Knowing

_____

ALBRAEKE - The Great

_____

ALUNR - The Light

_____

LOOK for the Word

Read the passage below. There are some special Islamic words in the passage. Make sure you know what they mean by putting them in the right blanks below.

For the Muslim Ummah the month of Ramadhan is very important. During that month they carry out a special Ibadah; the sawm. When the hilal of Ramadhan is seen, the month of fasting begins. It is a month in which Muslims try to do a great deal of Tilawah of the Qur'an, as well as recite Du'as and seek forgiveness for their sins. It is a month of Rahmah and Barakah from Allah.Fasting in the holy month helps a Muslim get Taqwa and learn to control himself. Also,fasting helps to get closer to Allah.

1. Blessings from Allah for the human being. _____

2. The Arabic word for fasting. _____

3. The new moon. _____

4. Mercy of Allah. _____

5. Recitation of Qur'an. _____

6. The Muslim Nation. _____

7. The ability to stay away from sins. _____

8. Worship of Allah. _____

36

Get the car going!!

Help the car reach home by answering the questions on the way as quickly as possible. Write the answers beside the signs.

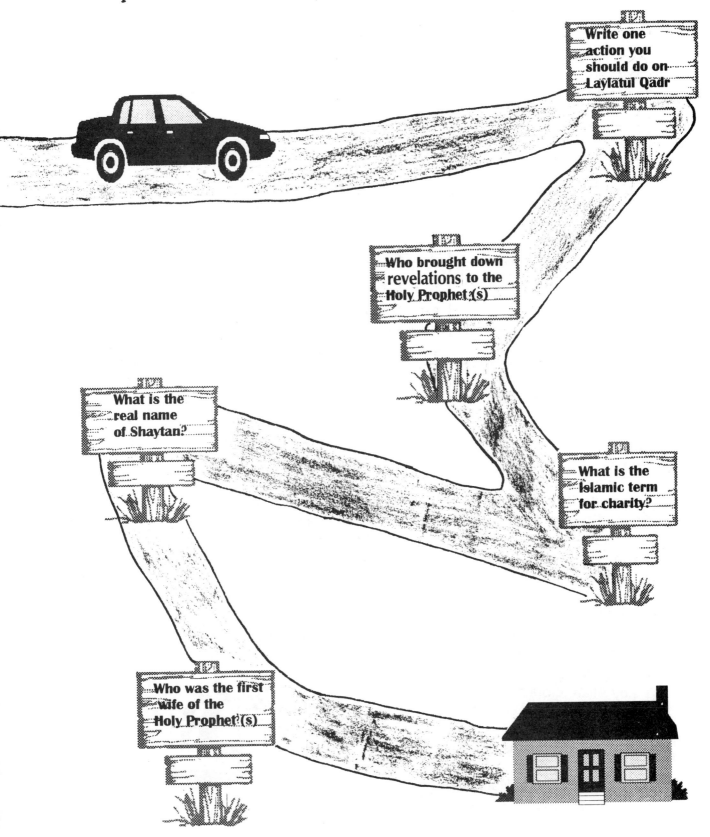

Write one action you should do on Laylatul Qadr

Who brought down revelations to the Holy Prophet (s)

What is the real name of Shaytan?

What is the Islamic term for charity?

Who was the first wife of the Holy Prophet (s)

ISLAMIC CROSSWORD

The crossword grid is numbered as follows: 1 (top row), 2, 3 (second row), 4, 5, 6 (third/fourth rows), 7, 8, 9, 10, 11, 12.

Clues

Across
1. Qur'an Al- _____
means the Noble Qur'an.
2. The Prophet who was given the miracle of the stick which turned into a snake.
6. Ayat 3 of Sura _____ (sura no:44) talks about the night of power.
7. _____ al-Fitr is given to the poor before Eid prayers.
8. The Prophet who was told by Allah to build an ark.
10. Laylatul _____ is better than a thousand months.
11. _____ is a means of talking to Allah.
12. The month after Ramadhan

Down
1. The holy place which is the qibla for all Muslims.
3. The name of Allah which means The Forgiver.
4. The early morning meal taken by those who wish to fast.
5. The Arabic word for Prophet.
9. Masjid al-_____ was the first qibla of the Muslims.

38

Preparing for Eid

Hameeda woke up to the sound of her 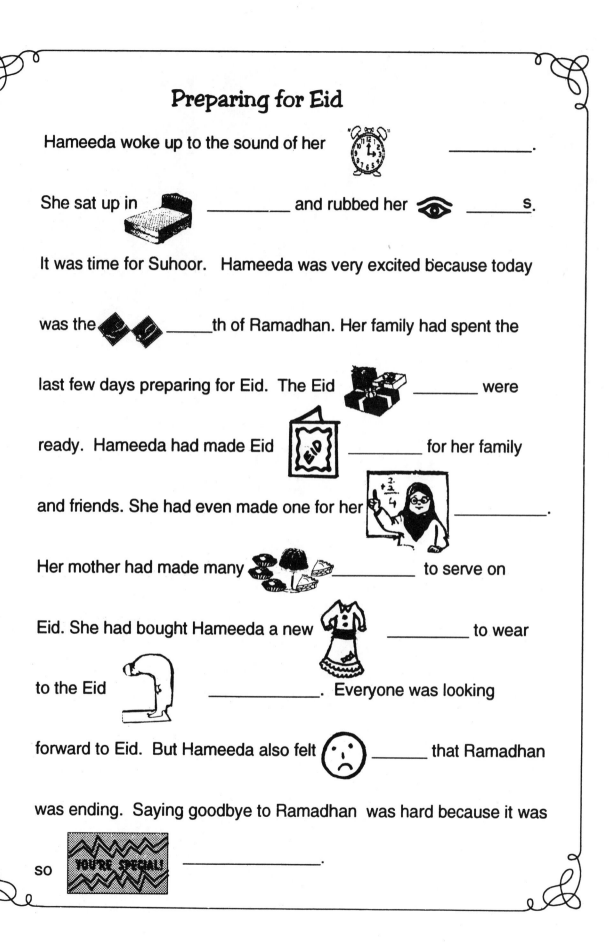 _____.

She sat up in _____ and rubbed her _____s.

It was time for Suhoor.   Hameeda was very excited because today

was the _____th of Ramadhan. Her family had spent the

last few days preparing for Eid. The Eid _____ were

ready. Hameeda had made Eid _____ for her family

and friends. She had even made one for her _____.

Her mother had made many _____ to serve on

Eid. She had bought Hameeda a new _____ to wear

to the Eid _____. Everyone was looking

forward to Eid. But Hameeda also felt _____ that Ramadhan

was ending. Saying goodbye to Ramadhan was hard because it was

so _____.

EID MUBARAK

What should we do for others on Eid?

THE MONTH OF RAMADHAN IS NOW OVER.
WE CELEBRATE EID BECAUSE WE HAVE BEEN ABLE TO OBEY THE COMMAND OF ALLAH IN THIS MONTH.
HOW ARE YOU GOING TO CELEBRATE EID?
CAN YOU MAKE A LIST OF THINGS TO DO ON EID?

Quran Challenge Game

A Fun Way to Learn About the Quran

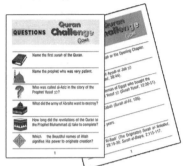

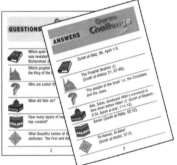

Books for Little Hearts!

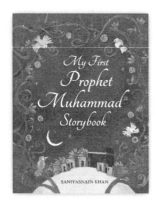

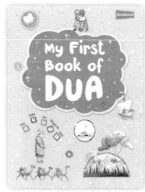

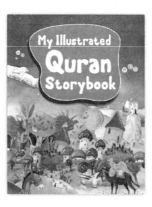

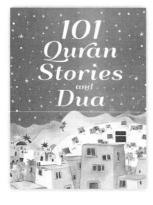

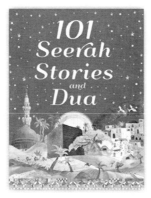

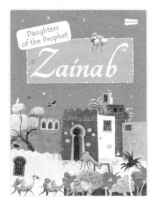

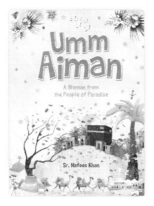

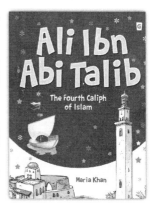

Goodword

www.goodwordbooks.com